Praise for *Pirates and Spooks, Beware!*

"*Pirates and Spooks, Beware!* is a collection of refreshingly fun, funny, and sometimes rascally poems, sure to delight elementary and middle school readers (and their teachers)! This entertaining collection of works from clever and talented poet Susan Weiner lends itself to enjoyable reading and a deeper study of poetic conventions, all the while providing subtle vocabulary, geography, history, and even meteorology lessons. Each poem reads equally well both silently and aloud, and could also provide a wonderful 'old school' memorization activity at the end of the unit of study. (Slam poetry, anyone?!) These rhyming poems appeal to the reader while telling a story in the most charming way. The lovely illustrations make them come alive, and thanks to Ms. Weiner's incredible imagination, we walk away smiling, thinking surely, 'Why, pirates (and spooks) are just like us!' Arghhh, matey... ENJOY!"

—Pat Talbert Smith, former Head of St. Francis Episcopal Day School and former Lower School Head/Assistant Head of St. Andrew's Episcopal School in Potomac, MD

"Many areas of study have been lost or seriously curtailed in the push to include the latest technology into classrooms across the country. One of these areas is poetry. Children do not read, study, or memorize much poetry as they have in past generations. Susan Weiner is doing her part in trying to alleviate this gap through this little volume of pirate poetry. Most kids go through a 'pirate phase' in their lives, and these poems capture the essence of the pirate lore quite fancifully. The fact that they also employ rhythm and rhyme are icing on the cake and serve to provide instruction in one of the basic skills of early literacy. I recommend this book for anyone interested in the drama and intrigue of pirates!"

—Carol Parent, learning specialist and former school administrator and classroom teacher

WRITTEN BY
SUSAN WEINER

ILLUSTRATED BY
BOBBIE KOGOK

Susan

May all your seas be calm! Avery and Eliana!
Blessings,
Bobbie Kogok
2018

BELLE ISLE BOOKS
www.belleislebooks.com

ISBN: 978-1-947860-15-5

LCCN: 2018950240

Cover and interior design by Michael Hardison. Illustrations by Bobbie Kogok.

Illustration design for "The Thing," "Wicked Wilhemina Winifred Jones," and "13" by Michael Hardison

Printed in the United States of America

Published by Belle Isle Books

BELLE ISLE BOOKS
www.belleislebooks.com

Dedication

The author and illustrator would like to dedicate this book to their families.

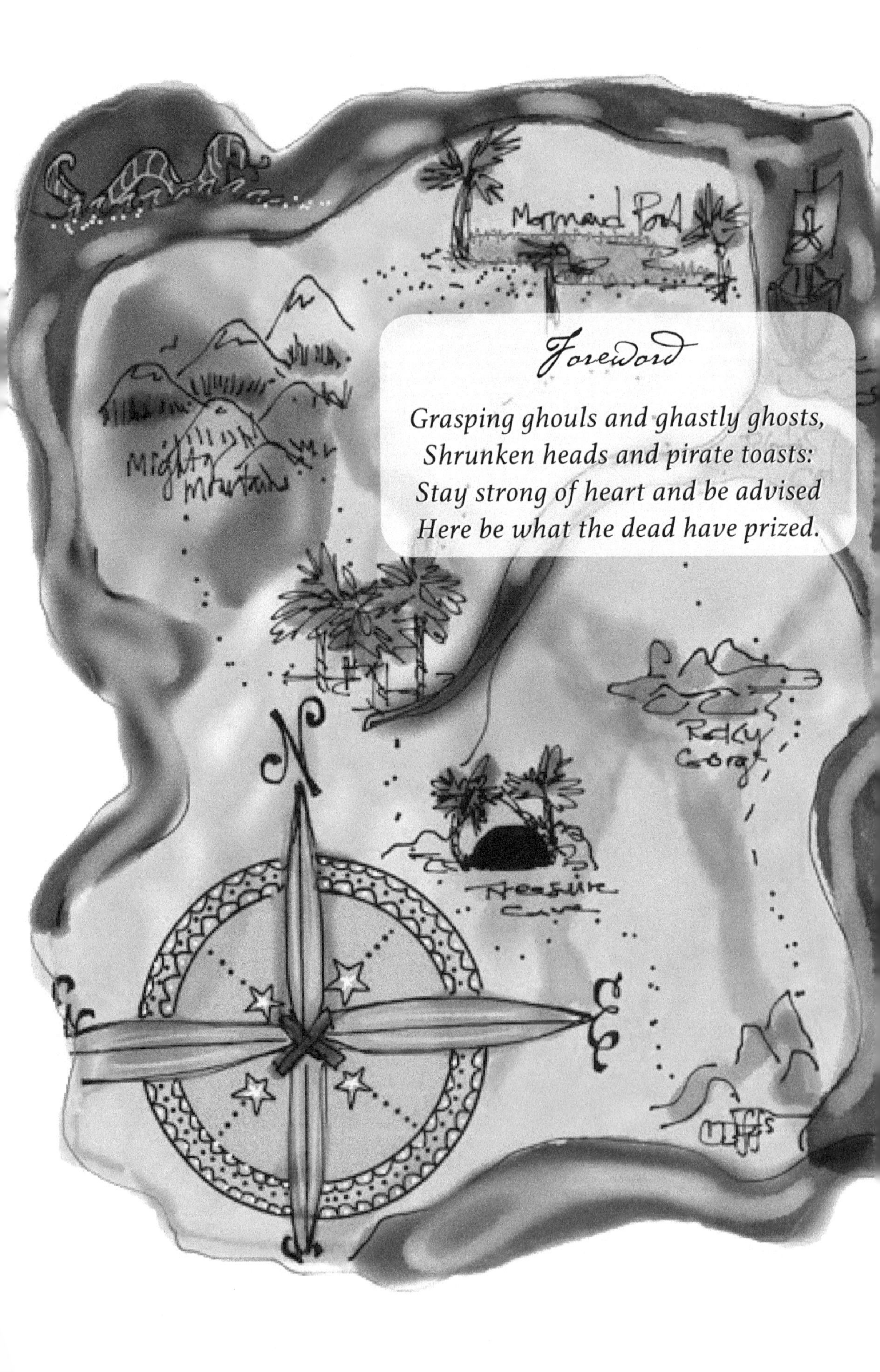

Foreword

Grasping ghouls and ghastly ghosts,
Shrunken heads and pirate toasts:
Stay strong of heart and be advised
Here be what the dead have prized.

Manifest

Stinky Pete

Stinky Pete was a tall, crooked fellow
Who wouldn't wash for weeks until
His new, white socks were mustard yellow.

He smelled just like a room of skunks,
But no one said a word, you see,
Because of what he held inside his trunks:

Six ivory-handled pistols to spare,
Seven deadly swords, and a dagger,
In case he dueled with a nobleman at the fair.

Stinky Pete, Stinky Pete wasn't always so neat.
His hammock had bugs, like flies and slugs,
And a terrible odor rose straight from his feet.

That fearsome rogue, scallywag, Stinky Pirate Pete
Made all the ladies hold their noses,
And the funk on his toes smelled just like bad meat.

Stinky Pete sailed the wild and foaming seas,
And into the deep blue, frothy waters,
He dove to beat the blasted, biting fleas.

Oh, Stinky Pete, who bathes within a wave?
Use soap, a sponge, and a tub, I hope,
As those hairy, scary knees surely need a shave.

Stinky Pete, connoisseur of rum buns and knives,
Fearsome of mien, the terror of seas—
Did you know, at one time, he had fourteen wives?

Stinky Pete, Stinky Pete wasn't always so neat,
His hammock had bugs, like flies and slugs,
And a terrible odor rose straight from his feet.

That fearsome rogue, scallywag, Stinky Pirate Pete
Made all the ladies hold their noses,
And the funk on his toes smelled just like bad meat.

The Lady Pirate

My rouge is a pretty, soft poppy red,
And a towering wig sits atop my head.
My gown's a brocade of celestial blue
So thick the bullets cannot pierce through.

My bustle is tied with bows and lace,
And I sneak with a certain stealthy grace.
I place my feet just so, here and there.
When I pass by, all the gentlemen stare.

I'm a pirate lady by day and by night.
My blade and I never flee from a fight.
I wear a pink sash set across my chest,
With knives and pistols at my breast.

Oh, Tortuga nights, where the palm trees are
And ships run adrift on the white sand bar.
Oh, Tortuga nights, where the pirates brawl
And duels are held at the governor's ball.

Tortuga nights follow Tortuga days,
Where treasure is stashed near turquoise bays,
And pirates take the hearts of tavern girls
With pure, white strands of oyster's pearls.

I stroll Tortuga streets on cobbled stones,
But stay away from restless pirate bones
That resurrect beneath full ocean moons
To swim to schooners nearing the dunes.

I've pale skin, freckles, and ocean-blue eyes.
My diamonds are dear as a Spanish prize.
My wig bears a ruby I stole from a duke;
At my back is a pirate captain's spook.

My blade and I never flee from a fight.

I like to fight in fashionable shoes.
(I take them off noble dames as I choose.)
In satins or silk, their beauty's the same,
But they look best when ships go up in flame.

Oh, Tortuga nights, where the palm trees are
And ships run adrift on the white sand bar.
Oh, Tortuga nights, where the pirates brawl
And duels are held at the governor's ball.

Tortuga nights follow Tortuga days,
Where treasure is stashed near turquoise bays,
And pirates take the hearts of tavern girls
With pure, white strands of oyster's pearls.

Although my corsets are covered in silk,
To me, rum's no more than mother's milk.
I can parry a boisterous mate gone mad
In the flouncy sleeves of Parisian fad.

With a split up my skirt, I swing my sword
To seize a merchant's sumptuous hoard.
When I bat my eyes at the county squire,
See the glance of his lady's jealous ire.

Oh Tortuga, Tortuga, sweet pirate's pride,
Ho, buccaneers, on the incoming tide.
The Caribbean Sea is your partner and guide,
And even the governors are on your side.

BLACKBEARD'S SONG

I have a heart as black as coal,
As dark as Satan's wicked soul.
I have a heart that's black as coal.

My blood is like a boiling sea.
I aim my pistol threateningly
And shoot my first mate in the knee.

I braid my beard up with my toes.
I tie it into fancy bows
From the new, red ribbons that I chose.

When I disembark for gold,
Give me all the jewels I can hold;
Spices and silks will all be sold.

At supper, serve me pickled fish—
It's a delicate feast of a dish.
For breakfast, bring me pickled fish!

My sword can split a mast—or you!
You'll see what parrying it will do
When it breaks the rigging right in two.

I fight in flames to foster dread;
See the smoke arise and spread
From fuses lit around my head.

I wear bright red rubies in my ears.
They look to all like bloody tears.
My fiendish eyes will rouse your fears.

I'm the worst a villain ever was.
Grenades are in my armpit fuzz,
And guzzling grog, that's what I does.

Because my heart's as black as coal,
As dark as Satan's wicked soul.
I have a heart that's black as coal.

I'M THE WORST A VILLAIN EVER WAS.

The Last Words of Pirate La Feet

These words are the last of Pierre La Feet,
A dreaded pirate who haunts your street:
I have matted hair and bloodshot eyes.
Best hide in sheets as I arrive.

Oh, I be the dreaded Pirate La Feet
With the dagger of vengeance sweet.
For the villain who pinched my gold,
I'll search 'til seas be glum and old.

On squally nights, I seek my treasure
Of lost doubloons you cannot measure.
I was robbed of rings that shone like stars
And masses of heavy, golden bars.

Oh, how my emeralds used to shine
And fill me more than a draught of wine.
Curse the day my wealth was gone
And my pirate chest showed only dawn.

So, swig some rum, roar 'til you're numb,
And test your knife with each cold thumb.
My voice is a gale in boughs of trees.
Your panes feel the beating of my seas.

For the villain who pinched my gold,

Like each typhoon, I know no bounds
And will not leash a hurricane's hounds.
Like mist, I rise from death's dark bog
And bawl like a madman soaked in grog.

If leaves are blown by howling storm,
See sheets of rain and my ghostly form.
There am I, as ships rupture and wreck
And waves overcome the heaving deck.

Oh, I be the dreaded Pirate La Feet
With the dagger of vengeance sweet.
For the villain who pinched my gold,
I'll search 'til seas be glum and old.

When lightning strikes, I stand my ground,
As thunder breaks with booming sound.
Like a vile bilge rat, I hunt hither and yon
For crowns and trinkets that are gone.

Oh, how my emeralds used to shine
And fill me more than a draught of wine.
Curse the day my wealth was gone
And my pirate chest showed only dawn.

In each gusty tempest and driving rain,
I cry for sapphires and seek 'em again.
These words are carved upon my grave,
So now you know the fortune I crave.

Like each typhoon, I know no bounds
And will not leash a hurricane's hounds.
Like mist, I rise from death's dark bog
And bawl like a madman soaked in grog.

I'll search 'til seas be glum and old.

THE THING

A Thing is a Thing, you must always remember,
Whether late in spring or early December.

A Thing's got fur that tickles its feet,
And it slurps up sodas that spill in the street.

A Thing, oh, a Thing's barely two feet high,
With vision gone bad in one bright red eye.

It makes rackets in closets in the dark of night,
As it snuffles for socks with delicious delight.

A Thing's got a nose like an elephant's snout,
And it sniffles for clothes you leave lying about,

Because to a Thing, laundry is tasty as cheese.
(Beneath a dusty bed, you may hear it sneeze.)

Now, a Thing's the color of root beer fizzes,
But it hates to read books and fails all quizzes.

With its eye that wobbles like the ground in Peru,
It dines on sneakers, a most delectable shoe.

Things are followed by starlets in disguise,
For in fashion and gowns, a Thing is wise,

Yet a Thing loves silk taffeta best of all.
If you catch it stealing, it may start a brawl.

Therefore, stuff that's lost in the washing machine
Is never really gone, as it may be seen:

From closets to wash, a Thing never ceases,
For a Thing finds your stuff and chews it to pieces.

A THING'S GOT FUR THAT TICKLES ITS FEET.

Thomasin James, Gentleman, Esquire, Sir

I

Thomasin James, Gentleman, Esquire, Sir
Took titles fit for legislature.
He stole them from lords and gallant men
Whose ancestors could write with a pen.

His favorite was Eustace Robespierre Ur,
Which belonged to the Duke of Devonshire.
Now, Thomasin James, Gentleman, Esquire, Sir
Was captain and cook of Ye Crooked Fir.

Of golden trinkets, he had exactly none,
Nor did he care for treasure by the ton;
But Thomasin James, Gentleman, Esquire, Sir
Pursued ancestries whose dates were sure.

He purloined medals but left rubies alone;
He hungered for crests and not a rough stone.
He followed his monarch's best warrior ships
To steal the "admiral" straight off their lips.

Oh, Thomasin James, Gentleman, Esquire, Sir,
Signor, sirrah, my liege lord, and monsieur.
The more names he took, the more hungry he got.
He'd be among princes, or he'd be among naught!

II

As a buccaneer, he stood in formidable shape
And hung from his shoulders a black silk cape.
He had fearsome eyes, as wild as the sea,
And hair gone gray quite becomingly.

He stood right as a rail, unbelievably straight;
Among nobility, it was a common trait.
Thomasin James, Gentleman, Esquire, Sir
Stood on his morals and would never stir.

Now, Thomasin James, Gentleman, Esquire, Sir
Enraged all the Knights of the Silver Spur
When he stole Baron von Petticoat Harrier Saint
And wrote "Count du Jour" on his prow in bright paint.

He boarded one ship and pinched a lady's name.
I can't pronounce it, but he took it just the same.
She offered her pearls, even threatened a fight,
But he regarded each tear with awful spite.

Oh, Thomasin James, Gentleman, Esquire, Sir
Loved titles more than a doctor could cure.
He stole so many his cabin grew full.
They gathered dust and rust and smelt of wool.

III

So he prowled the coasts of white-capped seas,
Carving initials on great passing trees.
Despite his titles—Gentleman, Esquire, Sir—
He stole like the seediest, low-down cur.

He took the Honorable Great and Lesser Tew
And wrapped it around the fancy Fenescue
De Wainscot Carlotta Governor Baxttus Roo,
That carried more names than carrots in stew!

One day, he sailed to the kingdom of India
To pilfer the papers to rule in Virginia.
Now, Thomasin James, Gentleman, Esquire, Sir
Was late to bed but generally first to stir.

By the glow of an early morning taper,
He examined his emblems collected on paper.
Thomasin James, Gentleman, Esquire, Sir:
That's where his attentions most often were.

To make his tomb at the House of the Lords,
Was the alluring goal he always aimed toward.
That Thomasin James, Gentleman, Esquire, Sir
Had seized upon names so he'd not die obscure.

TO PILFER THE PAPERS TO RULE IN VIRGINIA.

The Alligators

Down in the swampy, green marshes of Florida state,
Hear the squawk of a flamingo calling for its mate,

Where they have alligators bigger than a nobleman's steed,
With scales fastened down their back in a herringbone-tweed.

Why, alligators lie on the banks by the creeping moss
And use the sinews of their prey to do their daily floss.

They're dinosaurs that have lived two hundred million years
With teeth that are basically small and vicious spears.

Beware the running alligators who are quick as the gazelles.
They can eat right through a pirate ship and its bronze bell.

Alligators leap right out of the white and frothy water,
Resembling in every way a lion's savage slaughter,

For alligators rise with giant fishes in their jaws,
And those eyes, above the waterline, will cause you to withdraw.

They regard the world at every stage of evolution,
As if to say, I am the most ferocious contribution.

They will eat most anything that's vexed their meditation,
And their thrashing tails are signs of dreadful aggravation.

No bullet can harm those who are as cool as iguanas:
Those alligators show mercy like maddened piranhas.

If you give it a bit of thought, the moral's clear to see:
If you trek the Florida swamps, be sure you're quick to flee.

THEY CAN EAT RIGHT THROUGH A PIRATE SHIP AND ITS BRONZE BELL.

The Night of Scarabs

I

Oh, I am bound by bandages
Wound tightly 'round appendages.
My lips are twined in linen strips,
And gold rings loop my fingertips.

On the Night of Scarabs, all that's normal dies,
And mummies from their beds will arise.
My shrieks and groans will make you shiver;
Then you'll feel your legs begin to quiver.

I sleep inside a silent tomb,
Waking to a looming day of doom,
When I will stand with all my kin
And walk the world in tailored skin.

As I make those undead sounds,
You'll hear the howls of cats and hounds.
By the Eye of Horus, give me your wares.
Fog and mist linger in the air.

The Night of Scarabs is coming soon,
When my eyes will see the haunting moon.
Egypt's gods roam by homes tonight,
And the frogs will croak with a plague's delight.

II

On the Night of Scarabs, all Egypt will awake,
And her many chariots cause the ground to shake.
King Tut will swing the sharpest sword.
As Pharaoh, he bears the Crown of Lords.

On the Night of Scarabs, all that's normal dies,

On the Night of Scarabs, all that's normal dies,
And mummies from their beds will arise.
My shrieks and groans will make you shiver;
Then you'll feel your legs begin to quiver.

Even Anubis, with his jackal's head,
Feasts on Egypt's ancient beer and bread.
Now, scarab beetles stir from death again,
Sable as obsidian, like some black wolf's den.

As I make those undead sounds,
You'll hear the howls of cats and hounds.
By the Eye of Horus, give me your wares.
Fog and mist linger in the air.

Nothing stops the winged scarab, furious in his day.
In darkness, we reanimate in this way.
The gods of Egypt roam by homes tonight,
And the frogs will croak with a plague's delight.

III

Crocodiles, hippos, ibis, and the Nile
Invade the roads where sports cars drive in style.
A priest, a priestess, celebrants, and scribes!
Hieroglyphics on buildings we'll inscribe.

On the Night of Scarabs, all that's normal dies,
And mummies from their beds will arise.
My shrieks and groans will make you shiver;
Then you'll feel your legs begin to quiver.

Beneath the moon, each sacred heron flies,
And the earth exhales in deep and hallowed sighs.
Visit an ancient world of pyramids and tombs.
Find sarcophagi in old and treasured rooms.

And mummies from their beds will arise.

As I make those undead sounds,
You'll hear the howls of cats and hounds.
By the Eye of Horus, give me your wares.
Fog and mist linger in the air.

Ignore all the science of astrophysic labs
That peer past the Constellation of the Crab,
The gods of Egypt roam by homes tonight,
And the frogs will croak with a plague's delight.

IV

On the Night of Scarabs, never stay inside,
But let a ghost and witches be your guide,
Because pirates and some evil, nasty trolls
Wander the dark with bedlam in their souls.

On the Night of Scarabs, all that's normal dies,
And mummies from their beds will arise.
My shrieks and groans will make you shiver;
Then you'll feel your legs begin to quiver.

When you see a zombie shuffling down the street,
Don't let your heart speak directly to your feet.
On this night when candy runs like gold,
Even mummies in their wrappers will unfold.

As I make those undead sounds,
You'll hear the howls of cats and hounds.
By the Eye of Horus, give me your wares.
Fog and mist linger in the air.

Now you, too, can be old Egypt's king or queen
Because the Night of Scarabs falls on Halloween.
The gods of Egypt roam by homes tonight,
And the frogs will croak with a plague's delight.

A Pirate's Ode to Adventure

Oh, the roar of the waves is the compass of my soul.
I am one with the schooner's pitch and roll.
To storm each Spanish galleon's my principle goal;
Then I'll revel in all of the emeralds I stole.

Beneath black sails, pirates prowl upon deck.
As the parrot offers a squawk and a peck,
We sing songs of sailors who've gone off to wreck
Or been lost to the waves on a tempest's fierce trek.

Still, the swell of the sea's a sheer sapphire blue,
And the mystery of mermaids is out there, too.
The sails are set fire by a passionate crew,
Who follow a sun as gold as the loot they pursue.

Let lightning crack and thunder rumble away,
While storm clouds billow in purple and gray.
Merchants of the deep, tell your children to pray,
For I prowl past the tumult of the bay.

Oh, there are heaps of gold to satisfy my heart,
Star-bright gems that collectors call art,
And places not found on a nautical chart.
So, swing that sword if you're daring of heart.

We sail hundreds of leagues away from land.
When our wet toes forget the warm, white sand,
We'll measure our days by the sun's fierce hand,
And take our stand, a devilish pirate band.

Why, the ocean's monsters live in the deep. Beyond the sun, where the wobbegong weep.

Watch out for serpents who take cover by sea;
Larger than frigates, they bellow at me.
So, roar back at a head—after all, there are three—
For a brawl is now certain as a jeweled guarantee.

Love what you will; my love's the great ocean plain;
Each triton that tugs on our anchor and chain;
Each great octopus that yields a dark, inky stain;
And biscuits and beer, instead of fine wine and grain.

Let lightning crack and thunder rumble away,
While storm clouds billow in purple and gray.
Merchants of the deep, tell your children to pray,
For I prowl past the tumult of the bay.

Oh, there are heaps of gold to satisfy my heart,
Star-bright gems that collectors call art,
And places not found on a nautical chart.
So, swing that sword if you're daring of heart.

Why, the ocean's monsters live in the deep.
Beyond the sun, where the wobbegong weep,
Lobsters and starfish on the stippled sands creep
In the green kelp forest of Davy Jones' keep.

Soon the stars will sparkle in a velvet canopy,
Where they seem to shine especially for me.
They reflect in waters of the heaving, proud sea
Like pieces of treasure placed by hands carefully.

Now, the heart of a pirate's a-searching for gain;
It leaps into flight on the waves, its domain,
When the stars are numerous, like many sand grains,
And the love of the sea is its constant refrain.

With fiery eyes, we sail for barrels of gold,
For fine Spanish treasure from legends of old.
We drink 'til we revel in mischief untold
Or scrub down the ship and deck free of mold.

Oh, the timbers will groan and the sails bemoan
As we sail through the waters of oceans unknown
With a flag whose pennants stir panic when flown,
Embroidered on black with a skull and crossbones.

Coursing through fog are a convoy's stray ships.
Our cannon's quick fire tears their rigging to strips.
Seeing his sailor on the shattered deck slip,
The captain fumbles his teacup and breaks it to chips.

Oh, the timbers will groan and the sails bemoan
As we sail through the waters of oceans unknown
With a flag whose pennants stir panic when flown,
Embroidered on black with a skull and crossbones.

The screaming of men is the fiddle of war,
As the cutlasses clash and the musket fires roar.
So, surrender the deck to the blood and grim gore;
Sack the ship; take cutlery from every drawer.

Oh, the timbers will groan and the sails bemoan
As we sail through the waters of oceans unknown
With a flag whose pennants stir panic when flown,
Embroidered on black with a skull and crossbones.

We sail uncharted waters where sea monsters roam,
Where gigantic squids peer through the foam.
Where thunder can crack the sky's crystalline dome,
The fork of the lightning's our natural home.

Oh, the timbers will groan and the sails bemoan
As we sail through the waters of oceans unknown
With a flag whose pennants stir panic when flown,
Embroidered on black with a skull and crossbones.

Oh, the timbers will groan and the sails bemoan
As we sail through the waters of oceans unknown.

A Skull & Crossbones

Mermaids of the Hebrides

Come and see the mermaids swim through
The currents of the swirling Shetland Seas
As they rest beside deserted isles
And comb their hair with corals in the breeze.

A mermaid wants to give away her love
As your ship goes sailing, trailing by.
Keep your billows facing toward the wind,
And give your heart space enough to sigh,

Because the mermaids—yes, the mermaids—
Wave with deceitful eyes and treacherous hands,
Past a druid's stone and the misty Hebrides,
Near rocks where a schooner's graveyard stands.

So the mermaids sing, ***Come unto us***
And slip beyond the wretched hand of Fate.
Forget your long-gone years of tender youth
On a sunny deck as a ship's cabin mate.

Come, settle on a throne of curling waves
As silver seals claim the waters by your feet,
And aged Neptune, with his green sea-trident,
Has lobsters wave their tails to a tidal beat.

Consider the song of the narwhal whale:
In haunting timbres, she calls you from afar.
See the massive moon sharks, whose sparkling teeth
Shine bright beneath a rising polar star.

Oh sailor, with the daybreak in your eyes,
Long no more for your harbor in the bay,
Because, laddie, with a mermaid in your arms,
You'll drift to sleep as she begins to sway.

Beware golden tails that splash near shores
And the mermaid with a starfish in her hair;
For when the plunging waters come your way,
You're a plunder she doesn't want to share.

The eels will nibble gladly on your knees
Where jellyfish swim by in evening gowns,
And the fishes claim you as their reckoning
When a mermaid draws you ever farther down.

When rocks upend the ship like they were sharp knives,
Then comes a mermaid's sudden, deathly cries,
And she'll weave your hair into the cobalt of the sea
As on the ocean floor, your silent body lies.

Because, laddie, with a mermaid in your arms, you'll drift to sleep as she begins to sway.

WICKED WILHEMINA WINIFRED JONES

I

Wicked Wilhemina Winifred Jones
Fiendishly liked to play with old bones.
While boys built play castles out of stone,
She ambled in graveyards, all alone.
Wicked Winnie had hair as bright as gold
And dresses that splendid tailors sold.
She wore the sheerest of soft, silk socks
And rose-colored bows in her pretty locks.
Her complexion was truly whiter than snow,
With a nose that models longed to grow,
But her hands were like a black crow's feet:
Gnarled, withered, and coarse as wheat.
Her eyes were a mirror to her nasty heart,
Just wild enough to make a criminal start.

II

Wicked Wilhemina Winifred Jones
Loved cries of grief and grumbling groans.
She forced her maid to glide on tippy toes
And rudely tweaked her soft, little nose.
She kicked the butler right in his shin;
His awful shriek gave her a ghastly grin.
She growled at Granny's tea cup poodles
And put worms in Nanny's cup of noodles.
Mercury and mothballs might make you shiver,
But they were simply tonic for her rough liver,
Because Wicked Winnie was bad as sin
And vicious, even in her delicate chin.
Her tantrums were infamous down the street,
And all the servants knew she wasn't sweet.

III

Wicked Wilhemina Winifred Jones:
At squirrels, she hurled handfuls of stones.
She even threw baubles at bright little birds
And was far more atrocious than my words.
Wicked Winnie's soft, silk socks hid hairy feet
That she never combed or made quite neat.
She had two parents who loved her true,
But not even they knew quite what to do.
They took her to church, but she bit the priest.
Among quiet pews, she rose like a beast.
She was the worst of the honored Jones
And emptied two jars of her mother's cologne.
If she sighed, monsters from their closets fled.
If she smiled, parakeets fell over dead.

SHE HAD TWO PARENTS WHO LOVED HER TRUE, BUT NOT EVEN THEY KNEW QUITE WHAT TO DO.

IV

Wicked Wilhemina Winifred Jones,
With her hands just as ugly as crones',
Politely addressed dear Papa's friends.
Though her seething soul sought evil ends,
She spoke like spring to every squire,
Who'd soon find sweet lips hid such a liar.
In tutus, she twirled through cemeteries,
Where vultures flew like grand dignitaries;
Where vaults, beloved by Wicked Winnie,
Held the festering dead, from fat to skinny.
Some days, she stole flowers right off of graves
And dismissed the dead with royal waves.
In the end, not as beautiful as she seemed;
Even rats and roaches saw her and screamed.

I

Thirteen is the most sinister of all the signs.
If you want to greet a gremlin, it will do just fine.
(Don't forget to decant in a large beer stein
A dead man's dust when you hear the black cat whine.)
Thirteen is the hour when the knife glows red;
It's one past twelve, pursuant to all that's undead;
It's not the unspooling of Fate's fine thread,
But a communion of stumbling zombies instead.
So, scrawl dark emblems on the walls and floor
With curlicues and notes of a funeral score;
Simmer the toes of a swimmer with an apple core
In a brew that bubbles over with a tiger's roar
And the bristles of a fierce, rampaging boar.

Thirteen's a fairytale
without a happy end in sight.

II

Add a mummy's hands and a real dragon's claw,
The sparkling blue sapphire of a proud Persian shah,
The mark of the one beauty queen without any flaw,
And four loopholes to be found in congressional law.
Pour in two shots of absinthe with a drunkard's nose,
Scatter with flies and petals of a rotting rose,
Pepper with pages of distractingly purple prose,
And add a curse that a hardened convict chose.
Stir your potion thirteen times with the legs of a hen,
Finish with rings and fingers of fraternity men,
Chant by the thirteenth hour in an icky, oozing fen,
And summon all rank and reeking creatures again,
Like witches do in their dank, dark, and dripping den.

III

Thirteen's a fairytale without a happy end in sight,
Or a dawn as blind and black as a moonless night.
Thirteen doesn't care if you're of a certain height:
Nonsense will saturate all the verses you write.
Thirteen is a cemetery. It's certainly a grave.
It's that red dye number six in candies you crave;
It's drowning in a bathtub's shallow, soapy wave,
Or the scruffy feather of a dead Indian brave.
So, refrain from closing your eyes in the dark
Because sometimes, somewhere, looms a shark.
Number thirteen is a vicious and malicious mark.
It shuts the crypt against a softly singing lark
And shrivels all brightly-scented flowers in the park.

THE Hitchhiker

On a dark and dreary night
When even vultures take to flight,
When the rain comes splashing down
As if the lights might really drown,
Each heart knows that little touch of fear
As darkling things draw very near.
So, he roams beside the road,
Bearing such a heavy load.
Who wades beneath a broken sky
With thumb drawn out to draw you nigh?
Do you think we should stop the car
When we have to drive so very far?

In the back seat, he appears.
Your dad, who drives, displays no fear.
The man has pale but ponderous eyes,
Quite saucer-like and big as pies.
As he mumbles, baby quits her cries,
And all the doubt in Mother dies.
He's got beat-up shoes and mangy clothes,
A sweater-vest, and wormy hose.
He wears mittens, this strange newcomer,
But the thing is . . . well . . . it's summer.
Your mother greets him like a friend
And takes his scarf to darn and mend.

Now, he makes your groceries levitate,
And some eggs are lost to fate.
What rustles in dry, brown paper bags
As licorice squiggles, wiggles, and wags?
It's funny, but not so very sweet:
There goes your midnight treat
Of cookies flying toward his seat!
Perhaps he'd like some sandwich meat.
The baby laughs like there's a clown,
And Mama's eyes are looking down.
It's up to you to end this trick
Before you're empty-handed. Quick!

On a dark and dreary night
When even vultures take to flight,
When the rain comes splashing down
As if the lights might really drown,
Each heart knows that little touch of fear
As darkling things draw very near.
So, he roams beside the road,
Bearing such a heavy load.
Who wades beneath a broken sky
With thumb drawn out to draw you nigh?
Do you think we should stop the car
When we have to drive so very far?

"Help! Help!" you yell. "It's a ghost!
And he's got my Cinnamon Toast."
"Yes, my dear," says Mama gently.
"Eyes on the road," says Dad intently.
In tattered tweed, a tear rolls down
From the ghastliest ghoul in town.
See the bats that circle 'round his head,
Like the scary books you've read.
Then, he tips the brim of his silk hat
As if he'd have you stop and chat.
You must decide (despite your years)
If you are brave beyond your fears.

You see, the loneliest one of all
Is trailed by tempest and a squall.
Though he gleams like green swamp light,
He doesn't seem inclined to bite.
His heart has not really decayed;
Although his frame seems sort of frayed,
He hopes each child will understand
A ghost can crave an honest friend.
So, you reach and clasp his moldy hand
And share your Pringles from the can.
Now, because he shines so very bright,
He makes your heart come right alight.

You must decide (despite your years) if you are brave beyond your fears.

A Pirate Manifest

I

Oh, pirate ships haunt the Spanish Main,
Where palm trees grow higher than sugar cane,
And gold's what you get for the sale of grain
That comes by sea, despite the wind and rain.

On old parchment, here's a manifest,
Forgotten with coins in a pirate's chest,
Fixed with ribbons and the wax of a crest,
With drawings of maids slightly undressed.

Peer closely, now, and regard the script;
See how the ink has run where it's been dipped.
The print is as neat as engraving on a crypt
Where the amber stains of rum have dripped.

'Tis said a pirate steals your purse away
As you step onto that plank above the bay.
While the captain's on his knees to pray,
An outlaw strips that ship like it's harvest day.

Oh, pirate ships haunt the Spanish Main,
Where palm trees grow higher than sugar cane,
And gold's what you get for the sale of grain
That comes by sea, despite the wind and rain.

II

Pieces of eight, pearls to bankrupt a state,
A golden chain 'round the neck of a mate
Are not always found inside of each crate;
Yet goods keep the value of silver's weight.

Pirates won't pass up a pistol — that's first—
But they refuse woolen socks, which itch the worst.
Certainly, pirates sell anything cursed,
Like poison cups to cure a rich man's thirst.

Pirates love fur. There, I've said it out loud.
They long for ermine as white as a cloud,
But settle for calico, so pretty and proud,
For it claims the attention of a crowd.

Yes, they'll steal molasses, sugar, and bricks,
Raspberry jam (eight jars are better than six);
Lasses with curly locks (they'll take their picks),
With stolen umbrellas and a clock (if it ticks).

Pieces of eight, pearls to bankrupt a state,
A golden chain 'round the neck of a mate
Are not always found inside of each crate;
Yet goods keep the value of silver's weight.

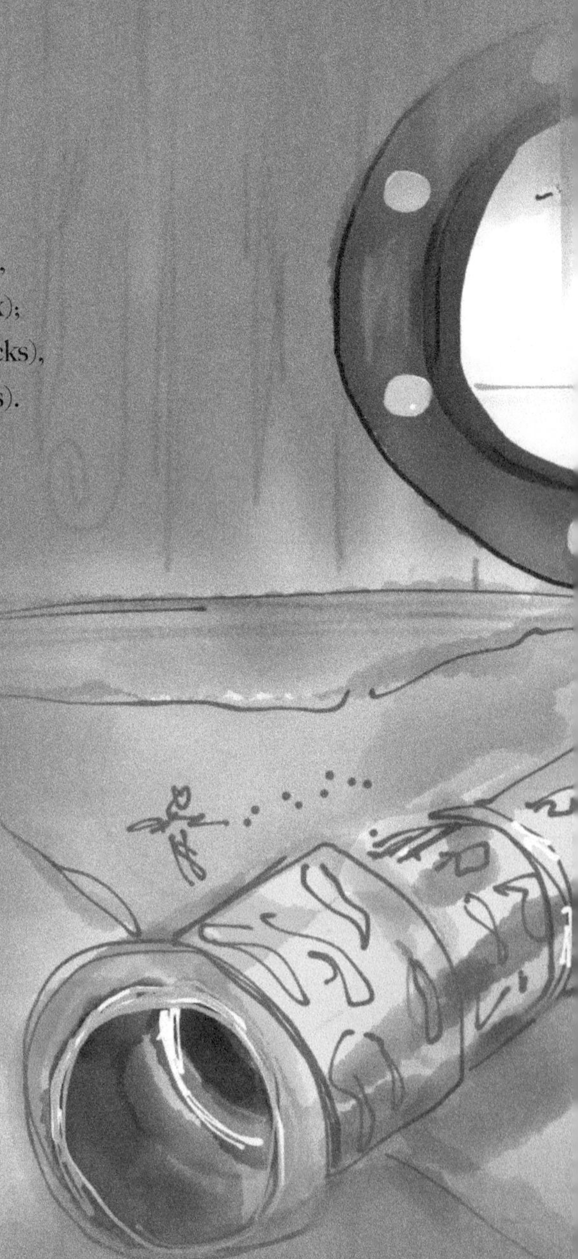

*What a ship can stock,
a pirate can steal,*

III

What a ship can stock, a pirate can steal,
Be it lavender soap or a large cheese wheel.
Coffee beans are as costly as citrus peel.
By a dock, where it's dim, you'll come to a deal.

Dark daggers with jewels will merit a sum,
But, for a merchant with ink on his thumb,
Tea leaves are as good as New England rum—
And a pirate will sell you a damson plum.

Pirates stash cargo below the board.
Imagine row boats where a ship is moored.
Under a moon that lights both mast and cord,
They prepare to sell each flint and sword.

Yes, everyone gets a little pirate gold,
From the governor to the merchant bold.
It's a life where you'll never grow old.
On the Caribbean Sea, waves heave and roll.

What a ship can stock, a pirate can steal,
Be it lavender soap or a large cheese wheel.
Coffee beans are as costly as citrus peel.
By a dock, where it's dim, you'll come to a deal.

*Be it lavender soap or a
large cheese wheel.*

HUNGRY IN

I

Oh, I was born a cannibal
With great, big, giant teeth,
And a palm branch twined with vines
Is what I dine beneath.

I lurk inside a jungle,
Below the great, green hanging eaves,
Where monkeys play hide and seek
In a canopy of leaves.

The tails of birds of paradise
Are scarlet red and azure blue,
And the sun-bright yellow finches
Have a song that calls to you.

The dappled deer have eyes
As deep as pools among the trees,
And all the hanging marsupials
Swing from their toes in the breeze.

See the orange-slipper orchids and
Daisies on the pine-loblolly floor,
Whose sweet perfume is borne to lands
Far away from our dear shore.

The fertile jungle blooms from
Swamps to the great and foaming seas.
All her creatures are friendly,
From the fire ants to the bees.

II

The jaguar and the panther
Will shield each tree frog from all harm,
And the boa constrictor won't
Make opossums sound a swift alarm.

By day, I climb up trees whose arms
Behold an eastern wind that blows.
Though I am a cannibal,
I've no taste for plump and meaty toes.

Instead, I make moist mushrooms
The biggest dumplings in my pot.
See here, I'll simmer these large
Root vegetables 'til they're hot.

Now, many pioneers have settled
On the new world of my shore
And found they hadn't any need
For satin garments that they wore.

So, they cast out moustache waxes
And lipsticks purchased from a store,
And left behind all lacey collars
Because they couldn't use them anymore.

So, we're bound and tied to buttercups,
To golden cubs and mother bears,
And, though I ought to dine on digits,
The frolicking fawns are in my care.

OH, I WAS BORN A CANNIBAL

THE JUNGLE

III

You see, I'm a vegetarian, and
The cannibal king can't understand
Why I croon to alligators
Who snooze upon the sun-warmed sand.

My heart is just a shepherd,
In the shadows only for a nap;
I trim the honeysuckle so
It's sweet as syrup from the sap.

If, by the mangrove leaf, you see me,
You really needn't turn and run.
I don't devour lords or princes,
Or gnaw on pirates just for fun.

It's that bib and grass-green lettuce
I like to stuff into my tarts.
But I prefer to boil, brine, and pickle
All chopped-up artichoke hearts.

So, when the jungle wakes to
The sun-kissed brightness of her days,
My cookbook says to flambé only
Vegetables in many kinds of ways.

Though I'm really supposed to be
A cannibal (with odd eating needs),
I'll be dancing with the flowers
And the budding ornamental weeds.

WITH GREAT, BIG, GIANT TEETH.

Acknowledgements

I would like to thank my editor, Christina Kann, for her fine eye in poetry and her expertise and thoughtful contribution in helping to revise the manuscript. Without her, my book would have been a lesser text. I am grateful to Robert Pruett, publisher of Belle Isle Books, for giving me this opportunity and for shepherding me through the process of publishing. I would like to extend my deepest thanks to Bobbie Kogok for illustrating this book with such charm and humor. She put up with a lot of changes with great grace. I also deeply appreciate Michael Hardison for his great talent in design and layout. If this book is attractive, it's due to their combined sense of whimsy and creative possibilities in the service of children's art. And finally, I would like to thank my mother, who listened to each poem time after time as I was engaged in rewriting, and who gave her sound advice on everything from meter to rhyme. She has truly been a partner in all the writing projects I have undertaken. Friends, family, and editors have all contributed to the pleasure I hope the reader will take in this book.

About the Author

Susan Weiner loves children's literature because ordinary rules do not apply, and anything can happen! Susan went to college in both England and America, but did her graduate study in history at UCLA. There, she kindled a passion for life and culture in the seventeenth century, especially in Great Britain. It was with great delight that, some years later, she began a book of pirate poems based on her studies. These days, Susan lives in Maryland near the Potomac River with one cat and many books.

About the Illustrator

Bobbie Kogok is an artist, illustrator, and children's book author. She has been painting and drawing since childhood. Recently, Bobbie has started creating her art on an iPad in an effort to save paper. In addition to illustrating for other authors, she has illustrated her own books, *The Moon, the Star, and the Firefly*; *If I Only Had a Penny*; and *Percival Pig Finds His Manners*. To see more of her work, visit www.bkpenandpaint.com.

CPSIA information can be obtained
at www.ICGtesting.com
Printed in the USA
FSHW01n0501111018
52866FS

9 781947 86015